Dharma Days

Art, Musings,
and Meditations
for the Spiritual Path

Dairyu Michael Wenger
2010 Calendar

Catalog No. L093
Published by Pomegranate Communications, Inc.
Box 808022, Petaluma CA 94975

Available in the UK and mainland Europe from Pomegranate Europe Ltd.
Unit 1, Heathcote Business Centre, Hurlbutt Road
Warwick, Warwickshire CV34 6TD, UK

Pomegranate also publishes the 2010 calendar *Buddhist Paintings* and more than 150 others in wall, mini wall, engagement, specialty, postcard, and 365-day tear-off formats. In addition to calendars, our extensive line of products and publications includes books, posters, postcards, notecards, invitations, thank you cards, magnets, mousepads, Knowledge Cards®, birthday books, journals, address books, jigsaw puzzles, designer gift wrap, stationery sets, and bookmarks. For more information or to place an order, please contact Pomegranate Communications, Inc., 800 227 1428, www.pomegranate.com.

Front cover: White-robed Water-Moon Avalokiteshvara, 2008
Seol Min (Korean, b. 1966)
Hanging scroll, ink and colors on cotton
Asian Art Museum of San Francisco, Gift of Seol Min, 2008.11
© 2008 Buddhist nun Seol Min. Courtesy of the Asian Art Museum.

Back cover: Buddha Amitabha with the eight great bodhisattvas, approx. 1300–1400
Korea, Goryeo dynasty (918–1392)
Hanging scroll, ink, colors, and gold on silk
The Avery Brundage Collection, B72D38
© Asian Art Museum of San Francisco. Used by permission.

Designed by Lisa Reid

Dates in color indicate US federal holidays.
Dates listed for all astronomical events in this calendar are based on Coordinated Universal Time (UTC),
the worldwide system of civil timekeeping. UTC is essentially equivalent to Greenwich Mean Time.
Moon phases and American, Canadian, and UK holidays are noted.

● NEW MOON ◐ FIRST QUARTER ○ FULL MOON ◑ LAST QUARTER

Dharma Days
Painting © Dairyu Michael Wenger

White-Robed Water-Moon Avalokiteshvara, 2008
Seol Min (Korean, b. 1966)
Hanging scroll, ink and colors on cotton
Asian Art Museum of San Francisco, Gift of Seol Min, 2008.11
© 2008 Buddhist nun Seol Min. Courtesy of the Asian Art Museum.

Introduction

Zen master Shogaku Shunryu said, "The secret of all the schools of Buddhism is to be present in the moment." *Dharma Days* is a day-to-day Buddhist engagement calendar, a reminder to be awake each day of the year. You can use it to help you focus your intention to show up for your life, or you can simply sit back and enjoy it.

The theme of this 2010 calendar is kindness and compassion, fundamental expressions of a Buddhist way of life. The inspiring images and words evoke and open the heart to a kinder and gentler way of life. Each month begins with a teaching, a poem, or a Zen story and suggests practices to manifest the specific teaching of that month.

The calendar's compelling images from the Asian Art Museum of San Francisco and The Newark Museum in Newark, New Jersey, are moving examples of the Asian legacy that shine through 2,500 years. Included, too, are a handful of my own inklings to remind us that the tradition is alive today.

Buddhism is often characterized as a religion of wisdom and compassion. As such, it is wise to be compassionate and compassionate to be wise.

May all beings be happy, kind, and compassionate!

—Dairyu Michael Wenger

Theme of the Year:

Kindness and Compassion

Kindness and compassion are at the heart of Buddhism throughout its history. The Bodhisattva of Compassion is Avalokiteshvara in Sanskrit, Kuan Yin or Guanyin in Chinese, and Kannon in Japanese—all of these terms literally mean "The Hearer of the Cries of the World." The bodhisattva started out as a male figure and increasingly became represented as a feminine figure. He/she has made a vow to leave no one behind and is often represented with a thousand eyes and arms, to see the world's suffering and to be able to respond effectively with many arms and hands.

In teaching his final class at the Department of East Asian Languages and Cultures at the University of California, Berkeley, Professor Lewis Lancaster made the following comment on what the many forms of Buddhism have in common:

> *How does a Buddhist act?*
>
> *Do I live like a Dharma Bum, believing in some form of renunciation and not using up the things of the world? Would I have to give up shopping . . . meat . . . sexuality?*
>
> *The frustrating thing . . . about the Buddhist tradition is that at every level, whenever we define it, we have already lost it.*
>
> *I ask myself how people can know that they are Buddhists. The one thing that all forms of Buddhism hold as their highest ideal is compassion. That seems as close to a universal answer as I can find . . . Buddhists, when they talk about compassion, say that if you are enlightened, you will have a deeper response to suffering. If insights do not lead to compassion, then it is not what the Buddha experienced at his enlightenment. This view makes an enormous difference.*

I invite you to use this calendar in whatever way you choose to bring about a kinder, more compassionate world.

Many blessings.

2010

JANUARY

s	m	t	w	t	f	s
					1	2
3	4	5	6	7	8	9
10	11	12	13	14	15	16
17	18	19	20	21	22	23
24	25	26	27	28	29	30
31						

FEBRUARY

s	m	t	w	t	f	s
	1	2	3	4	5	6
7	8	9	10	11	12	13
14	15	16	17	18	19	20
21	22	23	24	25	26	27
28						

MARCH

s	m	t	w	t	f	s
	1	2	3	4	5	6
7	8	9	10	11	12	13
14	15	16	17	18	19	20
21	22	23	24	25	26	27
28	29	30	31			

APRIL

s	m	t	w	t	f	s
				1	2	3
4	5	6	7	8	9	10
11	12	13	14	15	16	17
18	19	20	21	22	23	24
25	26	27	28	29	30	

MAY

s	m	t	w	t	f	s
						1
2	3	4	5	6	7	8
9	10	11	12	13	14	15
16	17	18	19	20	21	22
23	24	25	26	27	28	29
30	31					

JUNE

s	m	t	w	t	f	s
		1	2	3	4	5
6	7	8	9	10	11	12
13	14	15	16	17	18	19
20	21	22	23	24	25	26
27	28	29	30			

JULY

s	m	t	w	t	f	s
				1	2	3
4	5	6	7	8	9	10
11	12	13	14	15	16	17
18	19	20	21	22	23	24
25	26	27	28	29	30	31

AUGUST

s	m	t	w	t	f	s
1	2	3	4	5	6	7
8	9	10	11	12	13	14
15	16	17	18	19	20	21
22	23	24	25	26	27	28
29	30	31				

SEPTEMBER

s	m	t	w	t	f	s
			1	2	3	4
5	6	7	8	9	10	11
12	13	14	15	16	17	18
19	20	21	22	23	24	25
26	27	28	29	30		

OCTOBER

s	m	t	w	t	f	s
					1	2
3	4	5	6	7	8	9
10	11	12	13	14	15	16
17	18	19	20	21	22	23
24	25	26	27	28	29	30
31						

NOVEMBER

s	m	t	w	t	f	s
	1	2	3	4	5	6
7	8	9	10	11	12	13
14	15	16	17	18	19	20
21	22	23	24	25	26	27
28	29	30				

DECEMBER

s	m	t	w	t	f	s
			1	2	3	4
5	6	7	8	9	10	11
12	13	14	15	16	17	18
19	20	21	22	23	24	25
26	27	28	29	30	31	

The Buddhist deity White Tara, approx. 1400–1500
Nepal
Gilded copper repoussé
The Avery Brundage Collection, B60S22+
© Asian Art Museum of San Francisco. Used by permission.

Happy
New Year!

Dharma Days is starting
with a celebration of the
bodhisattva Never Despise,
who appears in chapter 20 of the Lotus
Sutra. This remarkable being does not
criticize anyone. He/she realizes that
everyone will be a Buddha one day.

If you vow to do this practice, don't be
discouraged. It is a difficult practice,
and if you can do it even for a short
period of time you may feel an incredible
buoyancy. If you find yourself judging,
don't add a criticism on top of a criticism.

Good luck!

Maitreya, the Buddha of the Future, 1800–1900
Mongolia
Thangka, colors and gold on cotton
The Avery Brundage Collection, B60D54

dharma practice

Dec ❖ Jan

BANK HOLIDAY (CANADA, UK)   *monday*

28 <small>362</small>

tuesday

29 <small>363</small>

wednesday

30 <small>364</small>

thursday

○ **31** <small>365</small>

NEW YEAR'S DAY   *friday*

1 <small>1</small>

saturday

2 <small>2</small>

JANUARY

s	m	t	w	t	f	s
					1	2
3	4	5	6	7	8	9
10	11	12	13	14	15	16
17	18	19	20	21	22	23
24	25	26	27	28	29	30
31						

sunday

3 <small>3</small>

Patchwork altar cloth
Central Asia or Tibet, thirteenth–fourteenth centuries
Silk brocade and lampas weave, embroidered edge
Collection of the Newark Museum
Purchase 1996 Estate of Gertrude Woodcock Simpson and Thomas L. Raymond Bequest Fund, 96.78

dharma practice

January

monday

4 4

tuesday

5 5

wednesday

6 6

thursday

◑ **7** 7

friday

8 8

saturday

9 9

sunday

10 10

ANUARY

m	t	w	t	f	s
				1	2
4	5	6	7	8	9
11	12	13	14	15	16
18	19	20	21	22	23
25	26	27	28	29	30

Throughout Space and Time
Painting © Dairyu Michael Wenger

January

monday

11 11

tuesday

12 12

wednesday

13 13

thursday

14 14

friday

● **15** 15

saturday

16 16

sunday

17 17

ANUARY

s	m	t	w	t	f	s
					1	2
	4	5	6	7	8	9
	11	12	13	14	15	16
	18	19	20	21	22	23
	25	26	27	28	29	30

Preaching Buddha, 1700–1900
Tibet
Thangka, ink and colors on cotton
The Avery Brundage Collection, B60D13+
© Asian Art Museum of San Francisco. Used by permission.

dharma practice

January

MARTIN LUTHER KING JR. DAY

monday

18   18

tuesday

19   19

wednesday

20   20

thursday

21   21

friday

22   22

saturday

◑ ## 23   23

DOGON'S BIRTHDAY

sunday

24   24

ANUARY

m	t	w	t	f	s
				1	2
4	5	6	7	8	9
11	12	13	14	15	16
18	19	20	21	22	23
25	26	27	28	29	30

Shell trumpet
Tibet, eighteenth century
Whelk horn, silver, coral
Collection of the Newark Museum
Gift of Orrin Hein in memory of Eleanor Olson, 1991, 91.574.13

January

monday

25 25

tuesday

26 26

wednesday

27 27

thursday

28 28

friday

29 29

saturday

○ **30** 30

sunday

31 31

ANUARY

m	t	w	t	f	s
				1	2
4	5	6	7	8	9
11	12	13	14	15	16
18	19	20	21	22	23
25	26	27	28	29	30

Compassion
Painting © Dairyu Michael Wenger and Max Gimblett

Compassion!

ompassion is usually defined as sympathy for the suffering of others (don't forget sympathy for you, too). Being able to appreciate the struggles that people are in can change our behavior toward them.

The opposite of compassion is ruthlessness: ignoring the effects we have on others to accomplish our goal.

There are several near enemies of compassion—thoughts and behaviors that may look like compassion but are far from it. For instance, feeling sorry for someone is far from feeling close to that person and may give you a sense of superiority. Similarly, getting depressed yourself when someone around you is feeling depressed is self-indulgence and helps no one.

Your homework this month (should you choose to do it) is to cultivate compassion without falling prey to its near enemies.

Shakyamuni, the historical Buddha, with the sixteen arhats, 1800–1900
Tibet
Thangka, one of seven images, colors on cotton
The Avery Brundage Collection, B62D38

February

monday

1 32

tuesday

2 33

wednesday

3 34

thursday

4 35

friday

◐ 5 36

saturday

6 37

sunday

7 38

FEBRUARY

s	m	t	w	t	f	s
	1	2	3	4	5	6
7	8	9	10	11	12	13
14	15	16	17	18	19	20
21	22	23	24	25	26	27
28						

The bodhisattva Avalokiteshvara (Guanyin) holding a vase, approx. 1900–1949
China
Nephrite
The Avery Brundage Collection, B60J235

dharma practice

February

monday

8 39

BODHIDHARMA'S BIRTHDAY

tuesday

9 40

wednesday

10 41

thursday

11 42

friday

12 43

saturday

13 44

VALENTINE'S DAY
LUNAR NEW YEAR

sunday

● 14 45

EBRUARY

m	t	w	t	f	s
1	2	3	4	5	6
8	9	10	11	12	13
15	16	17	18	19	20
22	23	24	25	26	27

Prayer wheel
Tibet, nineteenth century
Silver set with jade, rubies, and shell
Collection of the Newark Museum
Gift of Dr. Wesley Halpert and Mrs. Carolyn M. Halpert, 1984, 84.406

dharma practice

February

PRESIDENTS' DAY
BUDDHA'S PARIN (PARINIRVANA)

monday

15 46

MARDI GRAS

tuesday

16 47

ASH WEDNESDAY

wednesday

17 48

thursday

18 49

friday

19 50

saturday

20 51

sunday

21 52

The Buddha Amitabha and high monks of the Kagyu Order, approx. 1800–1900
Tibet; Kham area
Thangka, ink and colors on cotton
Gift of Girjia and Larry Brilliant, 2004.90

February

monday

◑ 22   53

tuesday

23   54

wednesday

24   55

thursday

25   56

friday

26   57

PURIM (BEGINS AT SUNSET)   *saturday*

27   58

sunday

○ 28   59

FEBRUARY

s	m	t	w	t	f	s
	1	2	3	4	5	6
7	8	9	10	11	12	13
14	15	16	17	18	19	20
21	22	23	24	25	26	27
28						

Eleven-headed bodhisattva Avalokiteshvara, approx. 1300
Western Tibet; Ladakh
Gilded bronze inlaid with copper and silver with turquoise semiprecious stones
The Avery Brundage Collection, B60S231
© Asian Art Museum of San Francisco. Used by permission

A koan is a public case, almost like a legal precedent, in which some issue of understanding is raised beyond the meaning of the words. This month, let's turn to Case 89 of the Blue Cliff Record, Avalokiteshvara's hands and eyes:

Yun Yen asked Tao Wu, "What does the bodhisattva of compassion use so many hands and eyes for?"
Wu said, "It's like groping for a pillow in the night."
Yen said, "I understand."
Wu said, "How do you understand it?"
Yen said, "All over the body are hands and eyes."
Wu said, "You have said quite a lot, maybe 80 percent."
Yen said, "What do you say, Older Brother?"
Wu said, "Throughout the body are hands and eyes."

Be alert to an opportunity to be of service.
Use whatever you have to be of help.
You don't necessarily know in advance how.
Do the best you can.

The bodhisattva Avalokiteshvara
(Gwanseeum Bosal), approx. 1600–1700
Korea, Joseon dynasty (1392–1910)
Hanging scroll, ink and colors on linen
The Avery Brundage Collection, B65D44
© Asian Art Museum of San Francisco
Used by permission

dharma practice

monday

1 60

tuesday

2 61

wednesday

3 62

thursday

4 63

friday

5 64

saturday

6 65

sunday

◗ **7** 66

MARCH

m	t	w	t	f	s
1	2	3	4	5	6
8	9	10	11	12	13
15	16	17	18	19	20
22	23	24	25	26	27
29	30	31			

Eleven-headed bodhisattva Avalokiteshvara, 1800–1900
China, Qing dynasty (1644–1911)
Gilded bronze
The Avery Brundage Collection, B60B138
© Asian Art Museum of San Francisco. Used by permission.

dharma practice

INTERNATIONAL WOMEN'S DAY

monday

8 67

tuesday

9 68

wednesday

10 69

thursday

11 70

friday

12 71

saturday

13 72

DAYLIGHT SAVING TIME BEGINS

MOTHERING SUNDAY (UK)

sunday

14 73

MARCH

m	t	w	t	f	s
1	2	3	4	5	6
8	9	10	11	12	13
15	16	17	18	19	20
22	23	24	25	26	27
29	30	31			

Avalokiteshvara
Tibet, eighteenth century
Appliqué silk damasks and brocades, cording, embroidery, pearls, and corals
Collection of the Newark Museum
Purchase 1957 Mr. C. Suydam Cutting and Mrs. C. Suydam Cutting Endowment Funds, 57.55

March

monday

● **15** 74

tuesday

16 75

ST. PATRICK'S DAY   wednesday

17 76

thursday

18 77

friday

19 78

VERNAL EQUINOX 17:32 UTC   saturday

20 79

sunday

21 80

MARCH

s	m	t	w	t	f	s
	1	2	3	4	5	6
7	8	9	10	11	12	13
4	15	16	17	18	19	20
1	22	23	24	25	26	27
8	29	30	31			

Bodhisattva
Tibet, second half of the thirteenth century
Cast copper alloy with silver and gold inlay
Collection of the Newark Museum
Purchase 1979 The Members' Fund, 79.442

March

monday

22 ₈₁

tuesday

◑ 23 ₈₂

wednesday

24 ₈₃

thursday

25 ₈₄

friday

26 ₈₅

saturday

27 ₈₆

MARCH

s	m	t	w	t	f	s
	1	2	3	4	5	6
7	8	9	10	11	12	13
4	15	16	17	18	19	20
1	22	23	24	25	26	27
8	29	30	31			

PALM SUNDAY
SUMMER TIME BEGINS (UK)

sunday

28 ₈₇

The Buddhist deity White Tara, 1800–1900
China; Beijing
Thangka, ink and colors on cotton
Transfer from the Fine Arts Museums of San Francisco, Gift of Katherine Ball, B72D44
© Asian Art Museum of San Francisco. Used by permission.

dharma practice

Mar ❦ Apr

PASSOVER (BEGINS AT SUNSET)   *monday*

29 88

tuesday

○ **30** 89

wednesday

31 90

thursday

1 91

GOOD FRIDAY   *friday*
BANK HOLIDAY (UK)

2 92

saturday

3 93

APRIL

m	t	w	t	f	s
			1	2	3
5	6	7	8	9	10
12	13	14	15	16	17
19	20	21	22	23	24
26	27	28	29	30	

EASTER   *sunday*

4 94

The Cosmic Buddha Ratnasambhava, 1200–1300
Tibet; Sakya
Thangka, colors on paper
Museum purchase, City Arts Trust Fund, 1991.2
© Asian Art Museum of San Francisco. Used by permission.

*Y*unmen, a tenth-century
Chinese Zen master, said,
"Medicine and disease
heal each other. The whole universe
is medicine. What is the self?" You're
probably wondering, what is medicine?
What is disease? And what is healing?

Sometimes poisons are medicine, literally
(e.g., chemotherapy). So don't hold back.
Anything may be a cure. Each moment
there is a potential to heal. In some ways,
your job is clearer than it's ever been.
Return to your body and mind and meet
this very moment! Disease and medicine
are all in a life's work.

Blessings to all.

Mandala of the Buddhist deity Sitatapatra Aparajita, 1700–1800
Tibet
Thangka, colors on cotton
The Avery Brundage Collection, B60D37
© Asian Art Museum of San Francisco. Used by permission.

dharma practice

April

5 95

tuesday

◑ **6** 96

wednesday

7 97

BUDDHA'S BIRTHDAY *thursday*

8 98

friday

9 99

saturday

10 100

sunday

11 101

m	t	w	t	f	s
			1	2	3
5	6	7	8	9	10
12	13	14	15	16	17
19	20	21	22	23	24
26	27	28	29	30	

Buddha's hand citron
China, Ming dynasty (1368–1644)
Nephrite
The Avery Brundage Collection, B60J9+
© Asian Art Museum of San Francisco. Used by permission.

April

monday

12 ₁₀₂

tuesday

13 ₁₀₃

wednesday

● **14** ₁₀₄

thursday

15 ₁₀₅

friday

16 ₁₀₆

saturday

17 ₁₀₇

sunday

18 ₁₀₈

dharma practice

April

monday

19 109

tuesday

20 110

wednesday

◐ **21** 111

EARTH DAY

thursday

22 112

friday

23 113

saturday

24 114

sunday

25 115

PRIL					
m	t	w	t	f	s
			1	2	3
5	6	7	8	9	10
12	13	14	15	16	17
19	20	21	22	23	24
26	27	28	29	30	

Mandala of Vajrabhairava, the conqueror of death, 1600–1700
Tibet; Ngor Monastery
Thangka, colors on cotton
The Avery Brundage Collection, B63D5
© Asian Art Museum of San Francisco. Used by permission.

Apr May

monday

26 116

tuesday

27 117

wednesday

○ ## 28 118

thursday

29 119

friday

30 120

saturday

1 121

sunday

2 122

In his poem "Please Call Me by My True Names," the contemporary Vietnamese teacher Thich Nhat Hanh movingly states his recognition that he carries the seeds of the best and worst of humanity in him.

Can you see an aspect of everyone in yourself?

Please Call Me
by My True Names

Don't say that I will depart tomorrow—
even today I am still arriving.

Look deeply: every second I am arriving
to be a bud on a Spring branch,
to be a tiny bird, with still-fragile wings,
learning to sing in my new nest,
to be a caterpillar in the heart of a flower,
to be a jewel hiding itself in a stone.

I still arrive, in order to laugh and to cry,
to fear and to hope.
The rhythm of my heart is the birth and death
of all that is alive.

I am a mayfly metamorphosing
on the surface of the river.
And I am the bird
that swoops down to swallow the mayfly.

I am a frog swimming happily
in the clear water of a pond.
And I am the grass-snake
that silently feeds itself on the frog.

I am the child in Uganda, all skin and bones,
my legs as thin as bamboo sticks.
And I am the arms merchant,
selling deadly weapons to Uganda.

I am the twelve-year-old girl,
refugee on a small boat,
who throws herself into the ocean
after being raped by a sea pirate.
And I am the pirate,
my heart not yet capable
of seeing and loving.

I am a member of the politburo,
with plenty of power in my hands.
And I am the man who has to pay
his "debt of blood" to my people
dying slowly in a forced-labor camp.

My joy is like Spring, so warm
it makes flowers bloom all over the Earth.
My pain is like a river of tears,
so vast it fills the four oceans.

Please call me by my true names,
so I can hear all my cries and my laughter at once,
so I can see that my joy and pain are one.

Please call me by my true names,
so I can wake up
and the door of my heart could be left open,
the door of compassion.

—Thich Nhat Hanh

Reprinted from *Call Me by My True Names* (1999)
by Thich Nhat Hanh, with permission of Parallax
Press, Berkeley, California, www.parallax.org.

So Many People to Be
Painting © Dairyu Michael Wenger

Buddha Amitabha with the eight great bodhisattvas, approx. 1300–1400
Korea, Goryeo dynasty (918–1392)
Hanging scroll, ink, colors, and gold on silk
The Avery Brundage Collection, B72D38
© Asian Art Museum of San Francisco. Used by permission.

dharma practice

May

BANK HOLIDAY (UK)

monday

3   123

tuesday

4   124

CINCO DE MAYO

wednesday

5   125

thursday

◑ 6   126

friday

7   127

saturday

8   128

MOTHER'S DAY

sunday

9   129

MAY

s	m	t	w	t	f	s
						1
2	3	4	5	6	7	8
9	10	11	12	13	14	15
16	17	18	19	20	21	22
23	24	25	26	27	28	29
30	31					

Lotus, from the flowers of the twelve months: June
Yun Bing (Chinese, 1670–1710)
Qing dynasty (1644–1911)
Album leaf, ink and colors on silk
The Avery Brundage Collection, B65D49.f

May

monday

10 130

tuesday

11 131

wednesday

12 132

thursday

13 133

friday

● 14 134

ARMED FORCES DAY

saturday

15 135

sunday

16 136

MAY

s	m	t	w	t	f	s
						1
	3	4	5	6	7	8
	10	11	12	13	14	15
	17	18	19	20	21	22
	24	25	26	27	28	29
	31					

Mandala of the Womb Realm, 1800–1900
Japan, Edo period (1615–1868)
Hanging scroll, ink and colors on silk
Gift of Gary Snyder, 2004.7
© Asian Art Museum of San Francisco. Used by permission.

May

monday

17 137

tuesday

18 138

wednesday

19 139

thursday

◑ **20** 140

friday

21 141

saturday

22 142

sunday

23 143

MAY

m	t	w	t	f	s
					1
3	4	5	6	7	8
10	11	12	13	14	15
17	18	19	20	21	22
24	25	26	27	28	29
31					

Full Moon Awakening
Painting © Dairyu Michael Wenger

dharma practice

May

VICTORIA DAY (CANADA)   *monday*

24 144

tuesday

25 145

wednesday

26 146

WESAK   *thursday*

○ ## 27 147

friday

28 148

saturday

29 149

sunday

30 150

MAY

m	t	w	t	f	s
					1
3	4	5	6	7	8
10	11	12	13	14	15
17	18	19	20	21	22
24	25	26	27	28	29
31					

The bodhisattva Avalokiteshvara (Guanyin), approx. 1100–1200
China, Song dynasty (960–1279)
Wood
The Avery Brundage Collection, B60S24+
© Asian Art Museum of San Francisco. Used by permission.

Kindness is to extend
ourselves regardless
of whether there is
anything in it for us. Its opposite is
hatred or ill will. Its near enemy is
to be kind in order to get something
in return or to win favor from someone.

Try being kind for the sake of kindness
itself. You may find you feel better as
a result.

Zhao Maoshu admiring lotuses
Ogata Korin (Japanese, 1658–1716)
Japan, Edo period (1615–1868)
Hanging scroll, ink and colors on paper
Museum purchase, B76D1

dharma practice

May Jun

monday

31 151

tuesday

1 152

wednesday

2 153

thursday

3 154

friday

◑ **4** 155

saturday

5 156

sunday

6 157

JNE

m	t	w	t	f	s
	1	2	3	4	5
7	8	9	10	11	12
14	15	16	17	18	19
21	22	23	24	25	26
28	29	30			

The bodhisattva Avalokiteshvara (Guanyin), approx. 1300–1400
China, Yuan (1279–1368) or Ming (1368–1644) dynasty
Wood with gilding and pigments
The Avery Brundage Collection, B61S37+
© Asian Art Museum of San Francisco. Used by permission.

June

monday

7 158

tuesday

8 159

wednesday

9 160

thursday

10 161

friday

11 162

saturday

● **12** 163

sunday

13 164

JUNE

m	t	w	t	f	s
	1	2	3	4	5
7	8	9	10	11	12
14	15	16	17	18	19
21	22	23	24	25	26
28	29	30			

The Diamond (Kongokai) mandala, one of a pair of mandalas of the Two World (Ryokai mandalas), probably 1700–1800
Japan, Edo period (1615–1868)
Hanging scroll, ink, colors, and gold on silk
Gift of Gary Snyder, 2004.8
© Asian Art Museum of San Francisco. Used by permission.

June

FLAG DAY   *monday*

14 165

tuesday

15 166

wednesday

16 167

thursday

17 168

friday

18 169

saturday

◑ **19** 170

FATHER'S DAY   *sunday*

20 171

m	t	w	t	f	s
	1	2	3	4	5
7	8	9	10	11	12
14	15	16	17	18	19
21	22	23	24	25	26
28	29	30			

Seated Buddha, approx. 800–900
Indonesia; probably central Java
Bronze
Gift of LEF Foundation, 1988.21
© Asian Art Museum of San Francisco. Used by permission.

dharma practice

June

SUMMER SOLSTICE 11:28 UTC

monday

21
172

tuesday

22
173

wednesday

23
174

thursday

24
175

friday

25
176

saturday

○ ## 26
177

sunday

27
178

JUNE

s	m	t	w	t	f	s
		1	2	3	4	5
6	7	8	9	10	11	12
13	14	15	16	17	18	19
20	21	22	23	24	25	26
27	28	29	30			

Jun ❧ Jul

monday

28 ₁₇₉

tuesday

29 ₁₈₀

wednesday

30 ₁₈₁

CANADA DAY (CANADA)   *thursday*

1 ₁₈₂

friday

2 ₁₈₃

saturday

3 ₁₈₄

INDEPENDENCE DAY   *sunday*

◗ **4** ₁₈₅

JULY

m	t	w	t	f	s
			1	2	3
5	6	7	8	9	10
12	13	14	15	16	17
19	20	21	22	23	24
26	27	28	29	30	31

Standing Buddha, approx. 700–800
Korea, Unified Silla dynasty (668–935)
Gilded bronze
The Avery Brundage Collection, B65B64
© Asian Art Museum of San Francisco. Used by permission.

*M*antra is a wonderful practice that can bring a great freshness into your life. I have used it when walking around as a way to cut into repetitious thought patterns.

When I was in my early twenties, I was a social worker in New York City. I had long hair and a beard, and I was on the softball team at work. One day while I was walking home, sweaty and a little disheveled after a hard game, I was reciting silently, "May all beings be happy." An older woman walking by me made a disparaging remark about my appearance. Perhaps because of the mantra, I didn't take it personally. I stopped, turned and faced the woman, and said very pleasantly, "Good morning." She paused, somewhat taken aback, and replied, "At least you're polite."

A little miracle.

The separation between us evaporated.

The Jain saint Rishabhanatha, 1623
India; Bihar or West Bengal state
Stone
The Avery Brundage Collection, B60S10

July

INDEPENDENCE DAY HOLIDAY

monday

5 186

tuesday

6 187

wednesday

7 188

thursday

8 189

friday

9 190

saturday

10 191

sunday

● 11 192

JULY

m	t	w	t	f	s
			1	2	3
5	6	7	8	9	10
12	13	14	15	16	17
19	20	21	22	23	24
26	27	28	29	30	31

Meditation Medley
Painting © Dairyu Michael Wenger

July

BANK HOLIDAY (N. IRELAND)

monday

12 ₁₉₃

tuesday

13 ₁₉₄

wednesday

14 ₁₉₅

thursday

15 ₁₉₆

friday

16 ₁₉₇

saturday

17 ₁₉₈

sunday

◐ **18** ₁₉₉

L Y

m	t	w	t	f	s
			1	2	3
5	6	7	8	9	10
12	13	14	15	16	17
19	20	21	22	23	24
26	27	28	29	30	31

Mandala of the Buddhist deity Vajravarahi, 1869
Nepal
Thangka, colors on cotton
The Avery Brundage Collection, B60D11+
© Asian Art Museum of San Francisco. Used by permission.

July

monday

19 200

tuesday

20 201

wednesday

21 202

thursday

22 203

friday

23 204

saturday

24 205

sunday

25 206

Ritual bell with five-pronged thunderbolt handle (gokorei), 1200–1333
Japan, Kamakura period (1185–1333)
Gilded bronze
The Avery Brundage Collection, B60B357b
© Asian Art Museum of San Francisco. Used by permission.

Jul ✿ Aug

ASALA-DHARMA DAY

monday

○ **26** 207

tuesday

27 208

wednesday

28 209

thursday

29 210

friday

30 211

saturday

31 212

sunday

1 213

AUGUST

s	m	t	w	t	f	s
1	2	3	4	5	6	7
8	9	10	11	12	13	14
15	16	17	18	19	20	21
22	23	24	25	26	27	28
29	30	31				

The Life of the Buddha, 1700–1800
Tibet
Thangka, ink and colors on cotton
Bequest of Marjorie Walter Bissinger, F2003.33.37
© Asian Art Museum of San Francisco. Used by permission.

"One desires pleasures and fears a hard life. These are sentiments one entertains before leading the so-called pleasurable or hard life. After one is in it, one tries to think of the envy and the fear and finds that they are gone. Then where are the pleasurable and unpleasurable thoughts after they are past? They seem to be like a sound, a shadow, a breeze, or a dream. Even these four things are somehow more tangible. Besides, how is one ever going to find happiness by countering one illusion with another illusion? I wish I could express this deep truth to you, but I cannot. "

—*Su Tungpo, August 5, 1088*

There you have it.

Seated Buddha, dated 338
China, Three Kingdoms period (221–419)
Gilded bronze
The Avery Brundage Collection, B60B1034
© Asian Art Museum of San Francisco. Used by permission.

dharma practice

August

BANK HOLIDAY (SCOTLAND)
CIVIC HOLIDAY (CANADA, MOST PROVINCES)

monday

2   214

tuesday

☽ 3   215

wednesday

4   216

thursday

5   217

friday

6   218

saturday

7   219

sunday

8   220

AUGUST

s	m	t	w	t	f	s
1	2	3	4	5	6	7
8	9	10	11	12	13	14
15	16	17	18	19	20	21
22	23	24	25	26	27	28
29	30	31				

Snuff bottle with Avalokiteshvara (Guanyin), dragon, and phoenix, 1800–1900
China, Qing dynasty (1644–1911)
Coral
Bequest of Isabella M. Cowell, B81M11.A-.B
© Asian Art Museum of San Francisco. Used by permission.

dharma practice

August

monday

9 ₂₂₁

tuesday

● **10** ₂₂₂

wednesday

11 ₂₂₃

thursday

12 ₂₂₄

friday

13 ₂₂₅

saturday

14 ₂₂₆

sunday

15 ₂₂₇

UGUST

m	t	w	t	f	s
2	3	4	5	6	7
9	10	11	12	13	14
16	17	18	19	20	21
23	24	25	26	27	28
30	31				

The bodhisattva Maitreya, 100–300
Pakistan; former kingdom of Gandhara
Schist
The Avery Brundage Collection, B60S597
© Asian Art Museum of San Francisco. Used by permission.

August

monday

◑ 16 228

tuesday

17 229

wednesday

18 230

thursday

19 231

friday

20 232

saturday

21 233

sunday

22 234

GUST

m	t	w	t	f	s
2	3	4	5	6	7
9	10	11	12	13	14
16	17	18	19	20	21
23	24	25	26	27	28
30	31				

Dragon Moon
Painting © Dairyu Michael Wenger

August

monday

23 ₂₃₅

tuesday

○ ## 24 ₂₃₆

wednesday

25 ₂₃₇

thursday

26 ₂₃₈

friday

27 ₂₃₉

saturday

28 ₂₄₀

sunday

29 ₂₄₁

GUST

m	t	w	t	f	s
2	3	4	5	6	7
9	10	11	12	13	14
16	17	18	19	20	21
23	24	25	26	27	28
30	31				

Seated bodhisattva Avalokiteshvara (Guanyin), approx. 1300–1400
China, Yuan (1279–1368) or Ming (1368–1644) dynasty
Gilded bronze
The Avery Brundage Collection, B60S566
© Asian Art Museum of San Francisco. Used by permission.

"*The inner tangle and the outer tangle, this generation is in a tangle. Who can untangle the tangle?*"

—Buddhagosa, fifth century

The world is always in a mess,
and we all have problems.
Do your best to untangle the tangle!

Standing monk, approx. 600–660
Korea; ancient kingdom of Baekje, Three Kingdoms period (57 BCE–668 CE)
Gilded bronze
Gift of Namkoong·Ryun, 2000.12
© Asian Art Museum of San Francisco. Used by permission.

dharma practice

Aug ✦ Sep

BANK HOLIDAY (UK EXCEPT SCOTLAND)

monday

30 242

tuesday

31 243

wednesday

◖ 1 244

thursday

2 245

friday

3 246

saturday

4 247

sunday

5 248

Head of a bodhisattva or deity, approx. 650–850
Thailand; Khu Bua, Ratburi province
Stucco
The James and Elaine Connell Collection of Thai Ceramics, 1989.6
© Asian Art Museum of San Francisco. Used by permission.

September

LABOR DAY (US, CANADA) _monday_

6 249

tuesday

7 250

ROSH HASHANAH (BEGINS AT SUNSET) _wednesday_

● **8** 251

thursday

9 252

friday

10 253

saturday

11 254

sunday

12 255

EPTEMBER

m	t	w	t	f	s
		1	2	3	4
6	7	8	9	10	11
13	14	15	16	17	18
20	21	22	23	24	25
27	28	29	30		

Buddhist altar (detail)
Newark Museum
Phuntsok Dorje, artist-in-residence 1988–1990
Consecrated by His Holiness, the fourteenth Dalai Lama, Sept. 23, 1990

September

monday

13 256

tuesday

14 257

wednesday

◑ **15** 258

thursday

16 259

YOM KIPPUR (BEGINS AT SUNSET)

friday

17 260

saturday

18 261

sunday

19 262

SEPTEMBER

m	t	w	t	f	s
		1	2	3	4
6	7	8	9	10	11
13	14	15	16	17	18
20	21	22	23	24	25
27	28	29	30		

Standing crowned Buddha with four scenes of his life, approx. 1050–1100
India; southern Magadha region; Bihar state
Stone
The Avery Brundage Collection, B65S11
© Asian Art Museum of San Francisco. Used by permission.

September

monday

20 <small>263</small>

INTERNATIONAL DAY OF PEACE

tuesday

21 <small>264</small>

wednesday

22 <small>265</small>

AUTUMNAL EQUINOX 03:09 UTC

thursday

○ ## 23 <small>266</small>

friday

24 <small>267</small>

saturday

25 <small>268</small>

sunday

26 <small>269</small>

EPTEMBER

m	t	w	t	f	s
		1	2	3	4
6	7	8	9	10	11
13	14	15	16	17	18
20	21	22	23	24	25
27	28	29	30		

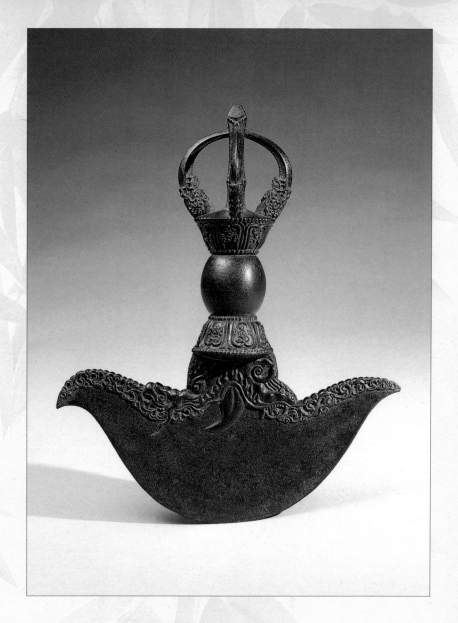

Chopper
Tibet, sixteenth century
Iron
Collection of the Newark Museum
Purchase 1954, 54.350

dharma practice

Sep ❋ Oct

monday
27 270

tuesday
28 271

wednesday
29 272

thursday
30 273

friday
◑ 1 274

saturday
2 275

sunday
3 276

OCTOBER

s	m	t	w	t	f	s
					1	2
3	4	5	6	7	8	9
10	11	12	13	14	15	16
17	18	19	20	21	22	23
24	25	26	27	28	29	30
31						

The Wheel of Life, 1800–1900
Tibet
Thangka, colors on cotton
Gift of Walter and Josephine Landor, 2001.49
© Asian Art Museum of San Francisco. Used by permission.

*I*n Japan the Obon ceremony for the dead is performed. Hungry ghosts—beings with large bodies and long, thin necks—are invited into the temple to be fed and healed. When the ceremony is over, they are asked to leave.

At the San Francisco Zen Center, we observe this ceremony on Halloween. We feel it is an apt cultural translation. Many people come in costume, and there is a big meal. The temple is also decorated with Halloween decorations.

May all beings be nourished!

Triangle Yogi
Painting © Dairyu Michael Wenger

dharma practice

monday

4 277

tuesday

5 278

wednesday

6 279

thursday

● 7 280

friday

8 281

saturday

9 282

sunday

10 283

Tsampa container
Tibet, thirteenth–fourteenth centuries
Iron with silver and gold inlay, brass fittings
Collection of the Newark Museum
Gift of Dr. Wesley Halpert and Mrs. Carolyn M. Halpert, 1988, 88.698

dharma practice

COLUMBUS DAY
THANKSGIVING DAY (CANADA)

monday

11 284

tuesday

12 285

wednesday

13 286

thursday

◑ **14** 287

friday

15 288

saturday

16 289

sunday

17 290

OCTOBER

m	t	w	t	f	s
				1	2
4	5	6	7	8	9
11	12	13	14	15	16
18	19	20	21	22	23
25	26	27	28	29	30

Amitayus
China; Chengde, Qing dynasty (1644–1911), reign of the Qianlong Emperor (1736–1795)
Thangka, colors on cotton
The Avery Brundage Collection, B60D24
© Asian Art Museum of San Francisco. Used by permission.

dharma practice

monday

18 291

tuesday

19 292

wednesday

20 293

thursday

21 294

friday

22 295

saturday

○ **23** 296

UNITED NATIONS DAY

sunday

24 297

The bodhisattva Avalokiteshvara (Guanyin) flanked by attendants, dated 570
China, Northern Qi dynasty (550–577)
Buddhist shrine, gilded bronze
The Avery Brundage Collection, B60B743
© Asian Art Museum of San Francisco. Used by permission.

dharma practice

monday

25 298

tuesday

26 299

wednesday

27 300

thursday

28 301

friday

29 302

saturday

◑ **30** 303

HALLOWEEN

SUMMER TIME ENDS (UK)

SEIJIKI CEREMONY (HUNGRY GHOST CEREMONY)

sunday

31 304

Milarepa (c. 1038–1122)
Tibet, fifteenth–sixteenth centuries
Cast brass with silver and jewel inlay
Collection of the Newark Museum
Purchase 1975 Sophronia Anderson Bequest Fund, 75.94

A monk asked Yun Men, "How is it when the tree withers and the leaves fall?" Yun Men responded, "Body exposed to the golden wind."

Vulnerability is very important in Buddhist practice. It leaves you open and motivated to change. If you are invulnerable you are not accessible.

Open your heart to things, and you may learn something.

Close your heart, and . . .

The bodhisattva Samantabhadra (Fugen), 1225–1250
Japan, Kamakura period (1185–1333)
Hanging scroll, ink, colors, and gold on silk
The Avery Brundage Collection, B66D2

November

monday

1 305

ELECTION DAY

tuesday

2 306

wednesday

3 307

thursday

4 308

friday

5 309

saturday

● 6 310

DAYLIGHT SAVING TIME ENDS

sunday

7 311

NOVEMBER

m	t	w	t	f	s
1	2	3	4	5	6
8	9	10	11	12	13
15	16	17	18	19	20
22	23	24	25	26	27
29	30				

The bodhisattva Avalokiteshvara, 1800–1900
Tibet
Thangka, colors on cotton
Gift of the Friends of Richard Davis, 1988.34
© Asian Art Museum of San Francisco. Used by permission.

dharma practice

November

monday

8 312

tuesday

9 313

wednesday

10 314

VETERANS DAY   *thursday*
REMEMBRANCE DAY (CANADA)

11 315

friday

12 316

saturday

◑ **13** 317

sunday

14 318

Full Moon Climbs Mountain
Painting © Dairyu Michael Wenger

dharma practice

November

monday

15 319

tuesday

16 320

wednesday

17 321

thursday

18 322

friday

19 323

saturday

20 324

OVEMBER					
m	t	w	t	f	s
1	2	3	4	5	6
8	9	10	11	12	13
15	16	17	18	19	20
22	23	24	25	26	27
29	30				

sunday

○ 21 325

The Eighteen Arhats (Lohans) (detail)
China, Qing dynasty (1644–1911), reign of the Qianlong Emperor (1736–1795)
Album, ink and colors on bodhi leaves
The Avery Brundage Collection, B65D4.17
© Asian Art Museum of San Francisco. Used by permission.

November

monday

22 ₃₂₆

tuesday

23 ₃₂₇

wednesday

24 ₃₂₈

THANKSGIVING

thursday

25 ₃₂₉

friday

26 ₃₃₀

saturday

27 ₃₃₁

sunday

◑ ## 28 ₃₃₂

Seated Buddha, approx. 1200–1350
Cambodia
Leaded copper alloy
The Avery Brundage Collection, B71S4
© Asian Art Museum of San Francisco. Used by permission.

*P*erhaps we should end
the year with a vow.
To vow is to go beyond,
to go from the visible to the invisible,
from habit to freedom, from the
conditioned to the unconditioned—yet
never to land in the invisible, the free,
or the unconditioned.

To vow is to go from what you know,
from your highest aspiration to where it
takes you, from what is possible to what
is inconceivable.

May kindness and compassion grace
your dharma days!

Vajradhara
Tibet, fifteenth century
Cast gilt copper with inlaid turquoise, coral, and lapis lazuli, traces of paint
Collection of the Newark Museum
Purchase 1970 The Members' Fund, 70.5

dharma practice

Nov ❈ Dec

monday

29 <small>333</small>

ST. ANDREW'S DAY (SCOTLAND)   *tuesday*

30 <small>334</small>

HANUKKAH (BEGINS AT SUNSET)   *wednesday*

1 <small>335</small>

thursday

2 <small>336</small>

friday

3 <small>337</small>

saturday

4 <small>338</small>

sunday

● 5 <small>339</small>

CEMBER

m	t	w	t	f	s
		1	2	3	4
6	7	8	9	10	11
13	14	15	16	17	18
20	21	22	23	24	25
27	28	29	30	31	

The bodhisattva Avalokiteshvara
of the Six Syllables, approx. 1758
China, Qing Dynasty (1644–1911),
reign of the Qianlong Emperor (1736–1795)
Hanging scroll, embroidery on silk
Gift of the Walter and Phyllis Shorenstein Fund, 1989.4
© Asian Art Museum of San Francisco
Used by permission

December

monday

6 340

tuesday

7 341

BUDDHA'S ENLIGHTENMENT DAY

wednesday

8 342

thursday

9 343

friday

10 344

saturday

11 345

sunday

12 346

CEMBER

m	t	w	t	f	s
		1	2	3	4
6	7	8	9	10	11
13	14	15	16	17	18
20	21	22	23	24	25
27	28	29	30	31	

Mahayana
Painting © Dairyu Michael Wenger

December

monday

◑ 13 ₃₄₇

tuesday

14 ₃₄₈

wednesday

15 ₃₄₉

thursday

16 ₃₅₀

friday

17 ₃₅₁

saturday

18 ₃₅₂

sunday

19 ₃₅₃

CEMBER

m	t	w	t	f	s
		1	2	3	4
6	7	8	9	10	11
13	14	15	16	17	18
20	21	22	23	24	25
27	28	29	30	31	

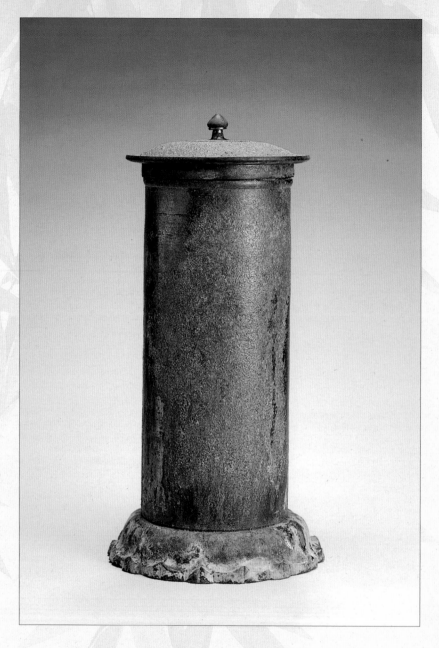

Sutra container, 1100–1200
Japan, Heian period (794–1185)
Bronze
Gift and Purchase from the Harry G.C. Packard Collection Charitable Trust in honor of Dr. Shujiro Shimada
The Avery Brundage Collection, 1991.78.A-.B
© Asian Art Museum of San Francisco. Used by permission.

dharma practice

monday

20 354

WINTER SOLSTICE 23:38 UTC | *tuesday*

○ **21** 355

wednesday

22 356

thursday

23 357

CHRISTMAS HOLIDAY | *friday*

24 358

CHRISTMAS | *saturday*

25 359

KWANZAA BEGINS | *sunday*
BOXING DAY (CANADA, UK)

26 360

ECEMBER

m	t	w	t	f	s
		1	2	3	4
6	7	8	9	10	11
13	14	15	16	17	18
20	21	22	23	24	25
27	28	29	30	31	

Six-armed form of the bodhisattva Avalokiteshvara (Nyoirin Kannon), 900–1100
Japan, Heian period (794–1185)
Gilding and pigments on wood
Gift of Mr. and Mrs. George F. Jewett, Jr., the Museum Society Auxiliary, and museum purchase, B71S3

Dec ❀ Jan

dharma practice

BANK HOLIDAY (UK)   *monday*

27 ₃₆₁

BANK HOLIDAY (UK)   *tuesday*

◐ ## 28 ₃₆₂

wednesday

29 ₃₆₃

thursday

30 ₃₆₄

NEW YEAR'S DAY HOLIDAY   *friday*

31 ₃₆₅

NEW YEAR'S DAY   *saturday*

1 ₁

sunday

2 ₂

JANUARY					
m	t	w	t	f	s
					1
3	4	5	6	7	8
10	11	12	13	14	15
17	18	19	20	21	22
24	25	26	27	28	29
31					

*S*oto Zen priest Dairyu Michael Wenger was born in Brooklyn in 1947. He moved to San Francisco in 1972 and became a member of the San Francisco Zen Center. He is currently in charge of Dharma group support at the Zen Center; he has served as dean of Buddhist studies and as president of the center. He received dharma transmission from Sojun Mel Weitsman and is the author of *Thirty-Three Fingers,* a collection of modern American koans, and editor of the book *Wind Bell.*

San Francisco Zen Center

San Francisco Zen Center was established in 1961 by Shunryu Suzuki Roshi (1904-1971) and his American students. Suzuki Roshi is known to countless readers as the author of the modern spiritual classic *Zen Mind, Beginner's Mind.* The purpose of San Francisco Zen Center is to make accessible and embody the wisdom and compassion of the Buddha as expressed in the Soto Zen tradition established by Dogen Zenji in thirteenth-century Japan and conveyed to us by Suzuki Roshi and other Buddhist teachers. Our practice flows from the insight that all beings are Buddha, and that sitting in meditation is itself the realization of Buddha nature, or enlightenment.

Today, San Francisco Zen Center is one of the largest Buddhist sanghas outside Asia. It has three practice places: City Center in the vibrant heart of San Francisco; Green Gulch Farm, whose organic fields meet the ocean in Marin County; and Tassajara Zen Mountain Center—the first Zen training monastery in the West—in the Ventana Wilderness inland from Big Sur. These three complementary practice centers offer daily meditation, regular monastic retreats and practice periods, classes, lectures, and workshops.

Zen Center is a practice place for a diverse population of students, visitors, laypeople, priests, and monks guided by teachers who follow in Suzuki Roshi's style of warm hand and heart to warm hand and heart. All are welcome. Zen Center programs also reach out to the community, helping prisoners, the homeless, and those in recovery; protecting the environment; and working for peace. Suzuki Roshi's disciples and students of his disciples now lead dharma groups around the country. Read more about our outreach programs on our website: www.sfzc.org.

Branching Streams

Branching Streams is a network of dharma centers in the tradition of Suzuki Roshi. Our intention is to encourage the practice of Soto Zen in inclusive and creative ways in centers large and small. The members of the group will stay in touch with each other and learn from each other's experience. Branching Streams exists to explore our interconnectedness, to nourish each other's practice, and to find new ways to benefit each other.

Here is a current listing of the Branching Streams sanghas. If your group is interested in joining this program, please e-mail us at branchingstreams@sfzc.org.

Big Sky Sangha, Paradise Valley, AZ; 602-820-5233

Arcata Zen Group, Arcata, CA; 707-826-1701

Tassajara, Carmel Valley, CA; 831-659-2229

Fresno River Zen Group, Clovis, CA; 559-877-2400

Vimala Sangha, Mill Valley, CA; 415-381-3015

Modesto Valley Heartland Zen Group, Modesto, CA; 209-573-8313

Monterey Bay Zen Center, Monterey, CA; 831-647-6330

Kannon Do Meditation Center, Mountain View, CA; 650-903-1935

Empty Nest Zendo, North Fork, CA; 559-877-2400

Beginner's Mind Zen Center, Northridge, CA; 818-349-7708

Dharma Eye Zen Center, Rohnert Park, CA; 707-869-3787

Iron Bell Zendo, Sacramento, CA; 916-456-7752

City Center, San Francisco, CA; 415-863-3136

Ocean Gate Zen Center, Santa Cruz, CA

Santa Cruz Zen Center, Santa Cruz, CA; 831-457-0206

Green Gulch, Sausalito, CA; 415-383-3134

Bamboo in the Wind, Sunnyvale, CA; 408-832-7690

All Beings Abode Zendo, Washington, DC; 202-265-1783

Beginner's Mind Zen Group, Tampa, FL

Floating Cloud Sangha, Boise, ID; 208-336-8176

Ancient Dragon Zen Gate, Chicago, IL; 312-925-9447

Udumbara Zen Center, Evanston, IL; 847-475-3264

Bozeman Zen Group, Bozeman, MT; 406-582-9090

Open Circle Sangha, Helena, MT; 406-442-4344

Chapel Hill Zen Center, Chapel Hill, NC; 919-967-0861

Elberon Zen Circle, Elberon, NJ; 732-241-3682

Brooklyn Zen Center, Brooklyn, NY; 718-701-1083

Empty Hand Zen Center, New Rochelle, NY; 914-636-1450

Austin Zen Center, Austin, TX; 512-452-5777

Houston Zen Center, Houston, TX; 713-869-1952

San Antonio Zen, San Antonio, TX; 210-287-6672

Notes

2011

JANUARY

s	m	t	w	t	f	s
						1
2	3	4	5	6	7	8
9	10	11	12	13	14	15
16	17	18	19	20	21	22
23	24	25	26	27	28	29
30	31					

FEBRUARY

s	m	t	w	t	f	s
		1	2	3	4	5
6	7	8	9	10	11	12
13	14	15	16	17	18	19
20	21	22	23	24	25	26
27	28					

MARCH

s	m	t	w	t	f	s
		1	2	3	4	5
6	7	8	9	10	11	12
13	14	15	16	17	18	19
20	21	22	23	24	25	26
27	28	29	30	31		

APRIL

s	m	t	w	t	f	s
					1	2
3	4	5	6	7	8	9
10	11	12	13	14	15	16
17	18	19	20	21	22	23
24	25	26	27	28	29	30

MAY

s	m	t	w	t	f	s
1	2	3	4	5	6	7
8	9	10	11	12	13	14
15	16	17	18	19	20	21
22	23	24	25	26	27	28
29	30	31				

JUNE

s	m	t	w	t	f	s
			1	2	3	4
5	6	7	8	9	10	11
12	13	14	15	16	17	18
19	20	21	22	23	24	25
26	27	28	29	30		

JULY

s	m	t	w	t	f	s
					1	2
3	4	5	6	7	8	9
10	11	12	13	14	15	16
17	18	19	20	21	22	23
24	25	26	27	28	29	30
31						

AUGUST

s	m	t	w	t	f	s
1	2	3	4	5	6	
7	8	9	10	11	12	13
14	15	16	17	18	19	20
21	22	23	24	25	26	27
28	29	30	31			

SEPTEMBER

s	m	t	w	t	f	s
				1	2	3
4	5	6	7	8	9	10
11	12	13	14	15	16	17
18	19	20	21	22	23	24
25	26	27	28	29	30	

OCTOBER

s	m	t	w	t	f	s
						1
2	3	4	5	6	7	8
9	10	11	12	13	14	15
16	17	18	19	20	21	22
23	24	25	26	27	28	29
30	31					

NOVEMBER

s	m	t	w	t	f	s
		1	2	3	4	5
6	7	8	9	10	11	12
13	14	15	16	17	18	19
20	21	22	23	24	25	26
27	28	29	30			

DECEMBER

s	m	t	w	t	f	s
				1	2	3
4	5	6	7	8	9	10
11	12	13	14	15	16	17
18	19	20	21	22	23	24
25	26	27	28	29	30	31

Students and teachers
Gods and Buddhas
Flowers, grasses and sanctuaries.
Acceptance or rejection

Each moment a seed is planted
and a flower blooms
Don't look elsewhere.

— *Dairyu Michael Wenger*